MAYBE YOU!

BY BROD BAGERT

POEMS & PLAYS FOR SCIENCE AS INQUIRY

Brod Bagert's Heart of Science
Illustrated by Natalia King
www.brodbagertsheartofscience.com

A word from Brod...

Science is the work of lots of people in each generation trying to figure out how nature works and what we can do with it. This book is an invitation to you to enter that world and maybe even become one of those people for your generation. The ideas in this book are pretty simple, but they're also extremely powerful, and once you get them in your head you'll be thinking like a scientist.

This book is full of poems and plays about science for you and your friends to read to each other. You're going to be amazed at just how much fun it can be to get crazy and go totally over-the-top when you act this stuff out. The best part is that you'll be learning science at the same time, really learning it, as in acing tests and making your teachers and parents happy.

Now right there some of you heard a voice in your head that said something like, "Yeah, that may be true for really smart kids, but what about me?" Please let me tell you about that little voice—it's not telling you the truth. It's not exactly lying because it thinks it's telling the truth, but what is says is still not truth. Human beings are smart, all human beings, and that includes you. If you're smart enough to play the average video game you're plenty smart enough to understand science. So please open that ferocious, great-white-shark brain of yours, and get ready to have a ton of fun hanging out with some great scientific thoughts.

TABLE OF CONTENTS

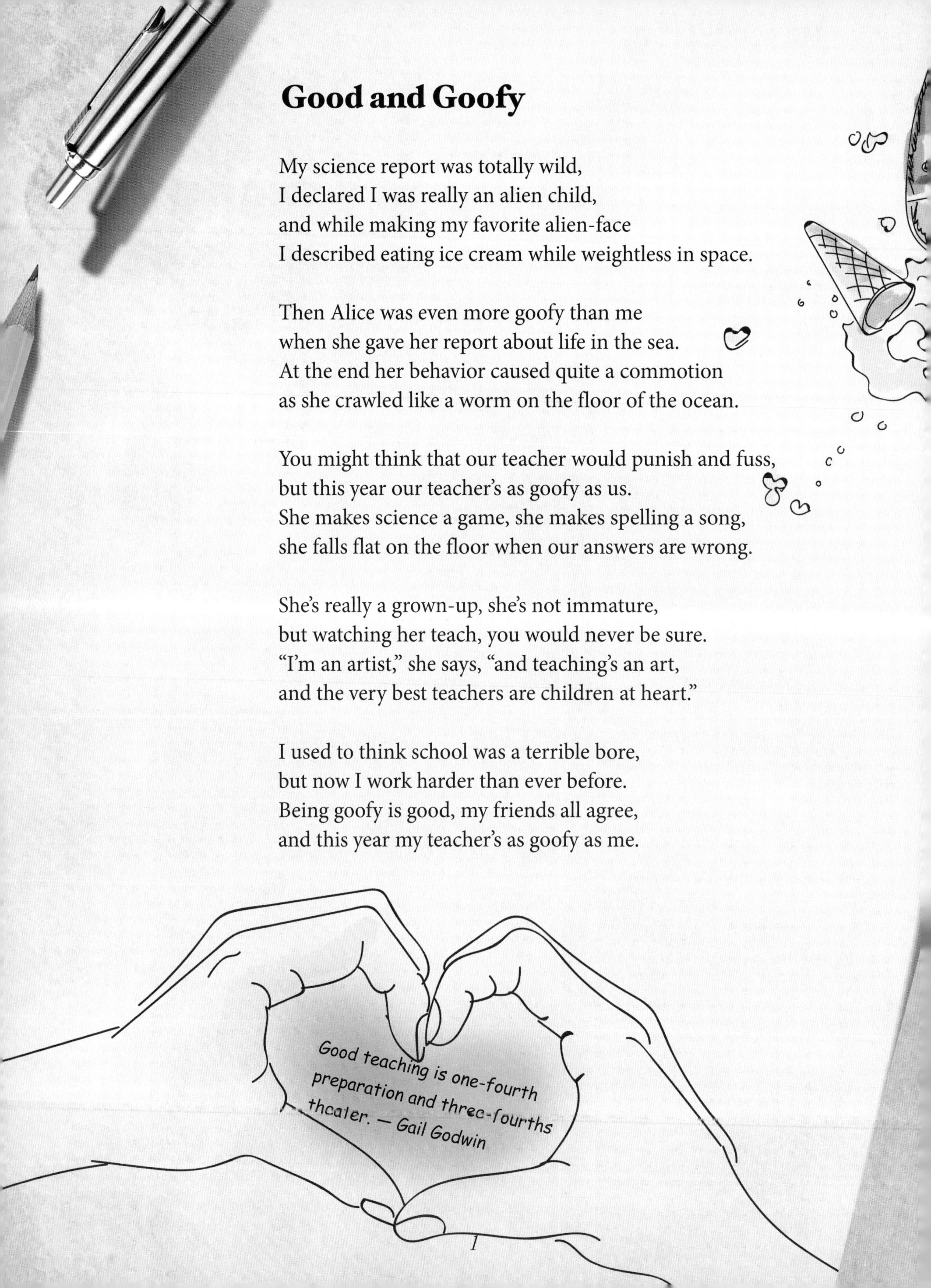

Good and Goofy

My science report was totally wild,
I declared I was really an alien child,
and while making my favorite alien-face
I described eating ice cream while weightless in space.

Then Alice was even more goofy than me
when she gave her report about life in the sea.
At the end her behavior caused quite a commotion
as she crawled like a worm on the floor of the ocean.

You might think that our teacher would punish and fuss,
but this year our teacher's as goofy as us.
She makes science a game, she makes spelling a song,
she falls flat on the floor when our answers are wrong.

She's really a grown-up, she's not immature,
but watching her teach, you would never be sure.
"I'm an artist," she says, "and teaching's an art,
and the very best teachers are children at heart."

I used to think school was a terrible bore,
but now I work harder than ever before.
Being goofy is good, my friends all agree,
and this year my teacher's as goofy as me.

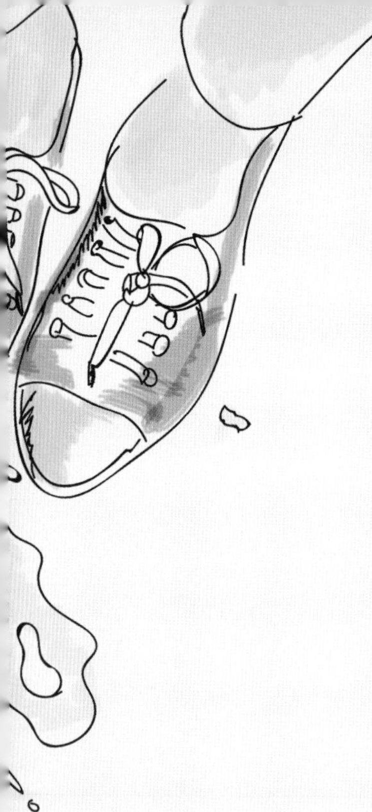

Someone Just Like You

"This book is baloney!" I said with a snarl,
unable to subdue it.
"Ten pages to say what magnets do,
but none say how they do it.
Run current through a wire, and
magnetic force is there.
But what exactly is this force
that travels through the air?"

My teacher turned and looked at me
with eyes that seemed to glow.
"Young lady," she said with a gentle smile.
"Some things we just don't know.
Magnetic force…gravitational force…
the forces within the atom…
the very light by which we see…
all things we don't yet fathom.
But we've learned a lot of stuff,
and we're learning more and more,
with each generation adding a bit
to what we knew before.
It's been going on for a very long time,
and there's lots more work to do,
but it always begins when a question is asked
by someone just like you."

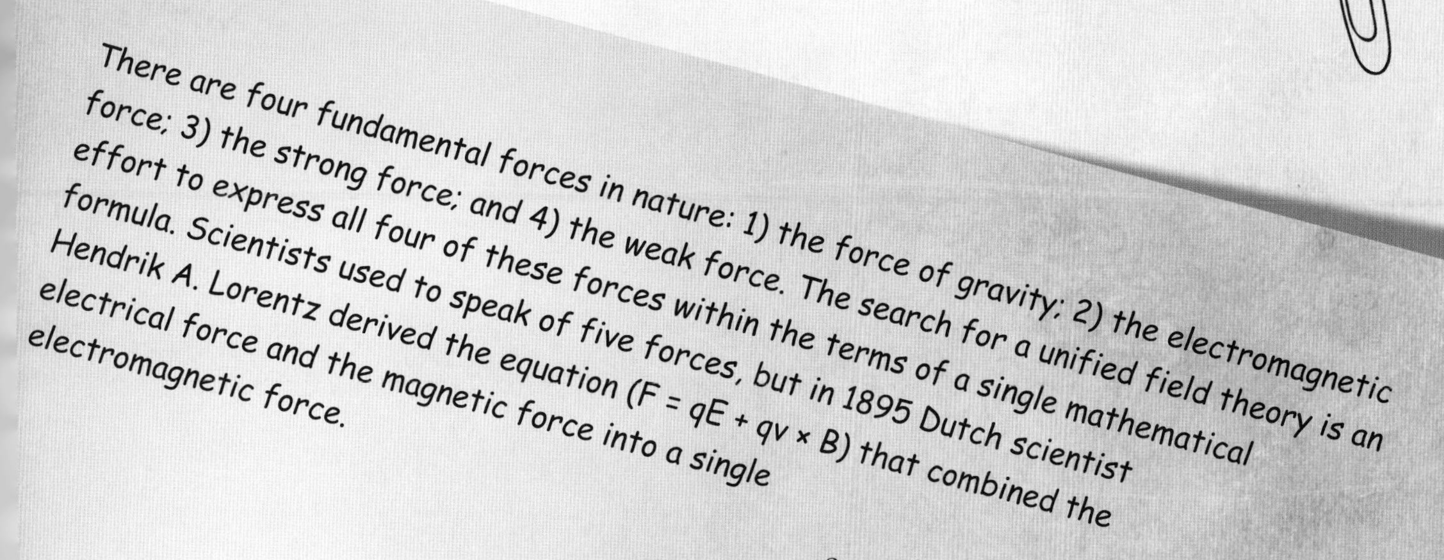

There are four fundamental forces in nature: 1) the force of gravity; 2) the electromagnetic force; 3) the strong force; and 4) the weak force. The search for a unified field theory is an effort to express all four of these forces within the terms of a single mathematical formula. Scientists used to speak of five forces, but in 1895 Dutch scientist Hendrik A. Lorentz derived the equation ($F = qE + qv \times B$) that combined the electrical force and the magnetic force into a single electromagnetic force.

Time Master
Ice Cream and the Universe

Big hand — MINUTES!
Little hand — HOUR!
Telling time — I HAVE THE POWER!
Time for ice cream.
Time for candy.
Telling time is very handy.

Big hand — MINUTES!
Little hand — HOUR!
Telling time — I HAVE THE POWER!
Time to play.
Time to run.
Telling time is so much fun.

Big hand — MINUTES!
Little hand — HOUR!
Telling time — I HAVE THE POWER!
Faster-slower, slower-faster,
telling time, I am the master.
Master of this clock appliance.
Next? I'M GOING TO MASTER SCIENCE!

Clocks are a very important scientific instrument. In most experiments, scientists use clocks to measure how long things take to happen. We think of Aristotle as a brilliant philosopher but he was also a scientist. About 2300 years ago he made a whopper of a mistake about the acceleration of falling objects. He concluded that a ten pound rock would fall twice as fast as a five pound rock, which is totally wrong. The world had to wait 1800 years for an Italian by the name of Galileo to prove that Aristotle was wrong and that a ten pound rock and a five pound rock would fall at the same speed.

If you're wondering why such a smart guy made such a big mistake there are two reasons. The first reason is that back in Aristotle's day there was no such thing as an experiment. Guys would just sit around and think about stuff and try to figure out what was true. (This is basically what we call deductive reasoning.) Galileo was one of the first scientists to do experiments to test theories. (We call this inductive reasoning.) The second reason for Aristotle's big mistake is that he didn't have a clock to measure how long it took for objects to fall. So even if he were inclined to put his hypothesis to the test (which he never was) he could not have conducted the experiment.

So once again we see how technology, in this instance clocks, and scientific knowledge walk hand in hand.

Stinky Feet
The US System of Measure

For everything I want to measure,
chicken feet or buried treasure,
here's a bit of happy news.
there's a unit I can use!

Measure water? I'm so smart.
Use a gallon! Use a quart!

Sweet potatoes? Let me check.
By the bushel! By the peck!

Measure ribbon? Thinking hard.
By the inch or by the yard.

What's the weather? Get it right.
Use degrees of Fahrenheit.

Chocolate candy! Crunchy sound!
I can eat it by the pound.

Tell me what you want to measure,
chicken feet or buried treasure,
Happy! Happy! Happy News!
THERE'S A UNIT I CAN USE!

I named this poem Stinky Feet because the US system of measurement is downright stinky. It gets the job done, but it's extremely hard to use, which is why only three countries in the world still use it: the U.S.A., Liberia, and Burma. The rest of the world has switched to the Metric system, because it's so much easier to use.

The Joy of "10"
or Time to Measure Up

An "inch" a "foot" a "yard" a "mile"-
familiar words that made me smile.
An "ounce" a "cup" a "pint" a "quart"-
it's how I learned it from the start.

Back then when I heard "kilogram"
it made my calculator jam.
It seemed so strange at first, but then
I learned it all divides by ten.

Metric is the easy way,
I learned it in a single day,
and now it's like I always knew it.
It's so easy. DO IT! DO IT!

In 1791 France adopted the first metric system which defined the length of a meter to be equal to one ten-millionth of the distance from the north pole to the equator.

In 1586 a Flemish mathematician by the name of Simon Stevin wrote that measuring in decimal-tenths was so much easier than ordinary fractions that it was only a matter of time before it became the universal system of weights and measures. Five hundred years later, I'm not so sure. Even though the Metric system is literally 10-times easier and has been adopted by most of the world, we in the USA keep hanging on to the old US system. Maybe you can surprise your friends around the world by learning and using both the US and the Metric systems!

METRIC MESASUREMENTS

0 1 2 3 4 5 6 7 8 9 10

Real Monsters

There's no such thing as monsters?
Please don't believe that lie.
I promise you, I've seen them,
they're as real as you and I.

The sight of the Spiny Assassin Bug
will fill you with dismay,
all covered with spikes and poison tubes
it sticks into its prey.

Dust mites crawling in your bed
to find their favorite treat—
those yummy flakes of human skin
that settle on your sheet.

And oh, the common maggot,
the larva of the fly—
with flesh tearing fangs they assemble in gangs
to eat us when we die.

With bulgy eyes and creepy thighs
and clinging claws they crawl,
real monsters by the billions
but they're very-very small.

Monsters don't exist?
It's a big-fat-dirty lie.
I saw them in a microscope,
as real as you and I.

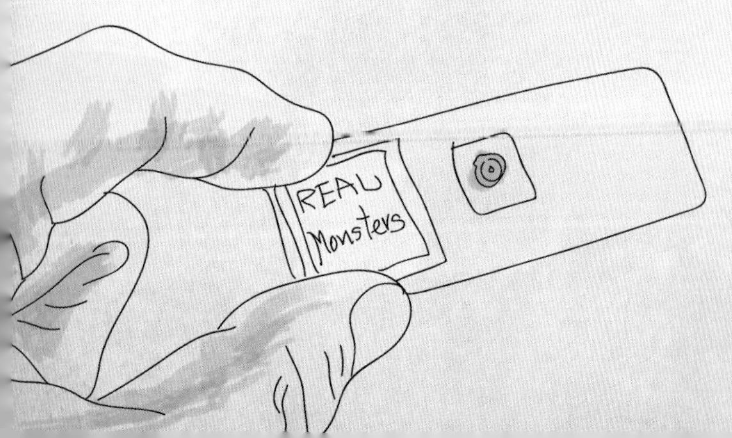

The microscope is my favorite example of the relationship between technology and science. Antony van Leeuwenhoek was a Dutch cloth merchant who made his own microscopes to examine cloth. His microscopes got better and better and in 1676 he looked into one of his microscopes and discovered germs (bacteria). Without a microscope there was no way to see germs, no way to know that they even existed. But once we could see them we began to study them. Two hundred years later another scientist by the name of Louis Pasteur made the scientific discovery that germs could cause disease. The world of modern medicine was born.

Robert Hooke made vast improvements in the magnification and resolution of early compound microscopes. He drew pictures of what he saw, and in 1665 he published his drawings in his now famous book, Micrographia.

My Curious Brain
The Ultimate Scientific Instrument

To measure weight? I never fail,
because I use a trusty scale.
To measure length or width or height
a simple ruler does it right.
For temperature, both hot and cold,
thermometers are good as gold.
To measure how much time goes by
a good clock never tells a lie.

To measure me, some think it's best
to see if I can pass a test.
But tests, which measure what I know,
can't say how much my brain will grow.
To measure that, it's plain to see,
check out my curiosity.

My brain is like a great white shark
always hunting in the dark.
So shout it—CURIOSITY!
Yes that is how you measure me.

Curiosity is the spark that fires the engines of science. It is impossible to overestimate its importance. Here are some of my favorite curiosity quotes.

"I think, at a child's birth, if a mother could ask a fairy godmother to endow it with the most useful gift, that gift would be curiosity."
— Eleanor Roosevelt

"Good education is not what fills your head with facts but what stimulates curiosity. You then learn for the rest of your life."
— Neil deGrasse Tyson (American Astrophysicist)

"The important thing is to never stop questioning. Curiosity has its own reason for existing."
— Albert Einstein

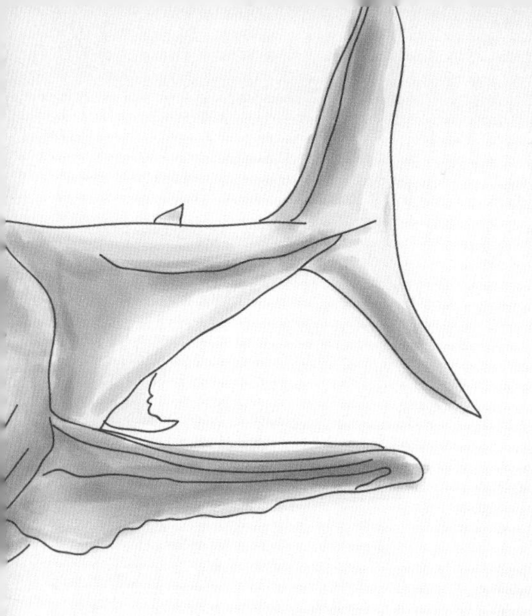

Just because something's in a book doesn't make it true, and in a world where almost everyone has access to the internet the habit of questioning the things we read is more important than ever.

Open Up

Some things are pretty tricky.
Did you ever wonder why
the sun gets big and orange
at the bottom of the sky?

What grows hair on your father's face?
What makes the black in tar?
Where do locusts come from?
How heavy is a star?

Well don't let questions scare you,
'cause you don't have far to look.
The whole world is your crystal ball
when you open up a book.

And if you find an answer there
there's one more thing to do.
It's time for you to question
if that answer's really true.

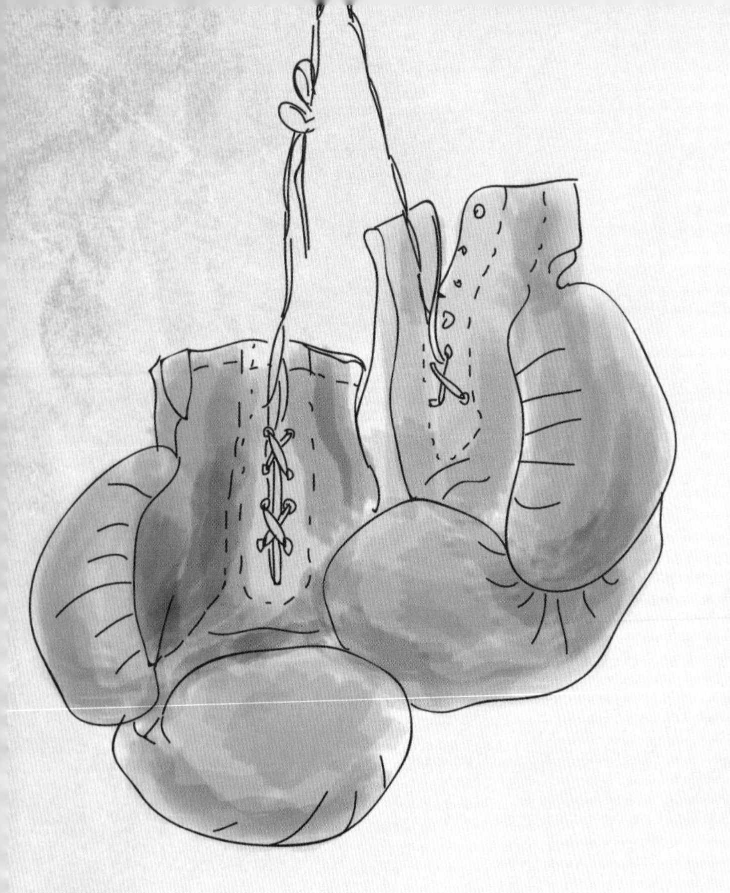

The Calculus Battle

It was such a dispute,
it was one of the worst,
over who had invented
the calculus first.

Newton or Leibniz?
Leibniz or Newton?
A whole lot of fightin',
and lots of disputin'.

They squabbled and fought
till the day that they died,
but neither had cheated,
and neither had lied.

And the Calculus question?
There seems little doubt
that Leibniz and Newton
both figured it out.

We don't usually think of math as a scientific tool, but much of modern science would be impossible without the kind of mathematics we call calculus, which was invented about 300 years ago. Back then there was a big controversy over who deserved credit, Sir Isaac Newton or Gottfried Wilhelm Leibniz. Science historians have since studied the papers of both men and concluded that they both arrived at the discovery independently.

Now here's the cool part: this happens all the time. In the 1700s Antoine Lavoisier gets credit for the discovery of oxygen, but three years earlier Joseph Priestley had isolated oxygen and described its properties, though he misunderstood what it was. In the 1800s Charles Darwin gets credit for the theory of evolution by natural selection, but a naturalist by the name of Alfred Russel Wallace had come up with the idea at about the same time.

So here's a question for you to think about. Why does this happen? Why is it that two or more scientists in the same generation come up with the same discovery at the same time? Here's a hint. It's a quote from a letter Isaac Newton wrote to Robert Hooke in 1676. "If I have seen a little further it is by standing on the shoulders of giants."

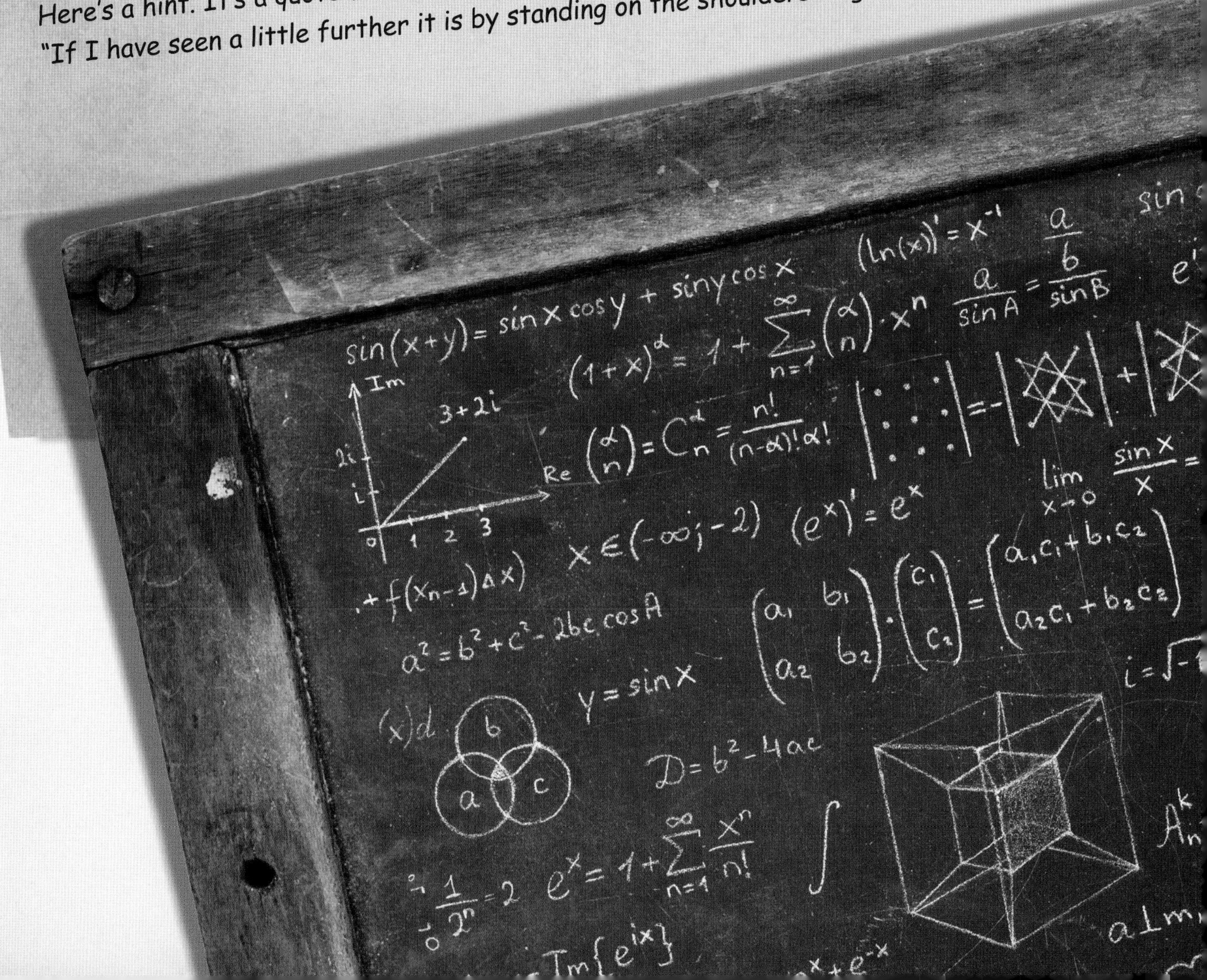

Questions and Answers

Who? What? When? and Where?
are questions we always allow,
but my very favorite question to ask
is the ever-spectacular…HOW?

And many a HOW? has no answer,
so we're left in the shadow of doubt,
which makes it fun when you're the one
who gets to figure it out.

A world where all questions have answers
would be an unbearable bore,
and the joy of each life, amidst struggle and strife,
is to answer a little bit more.

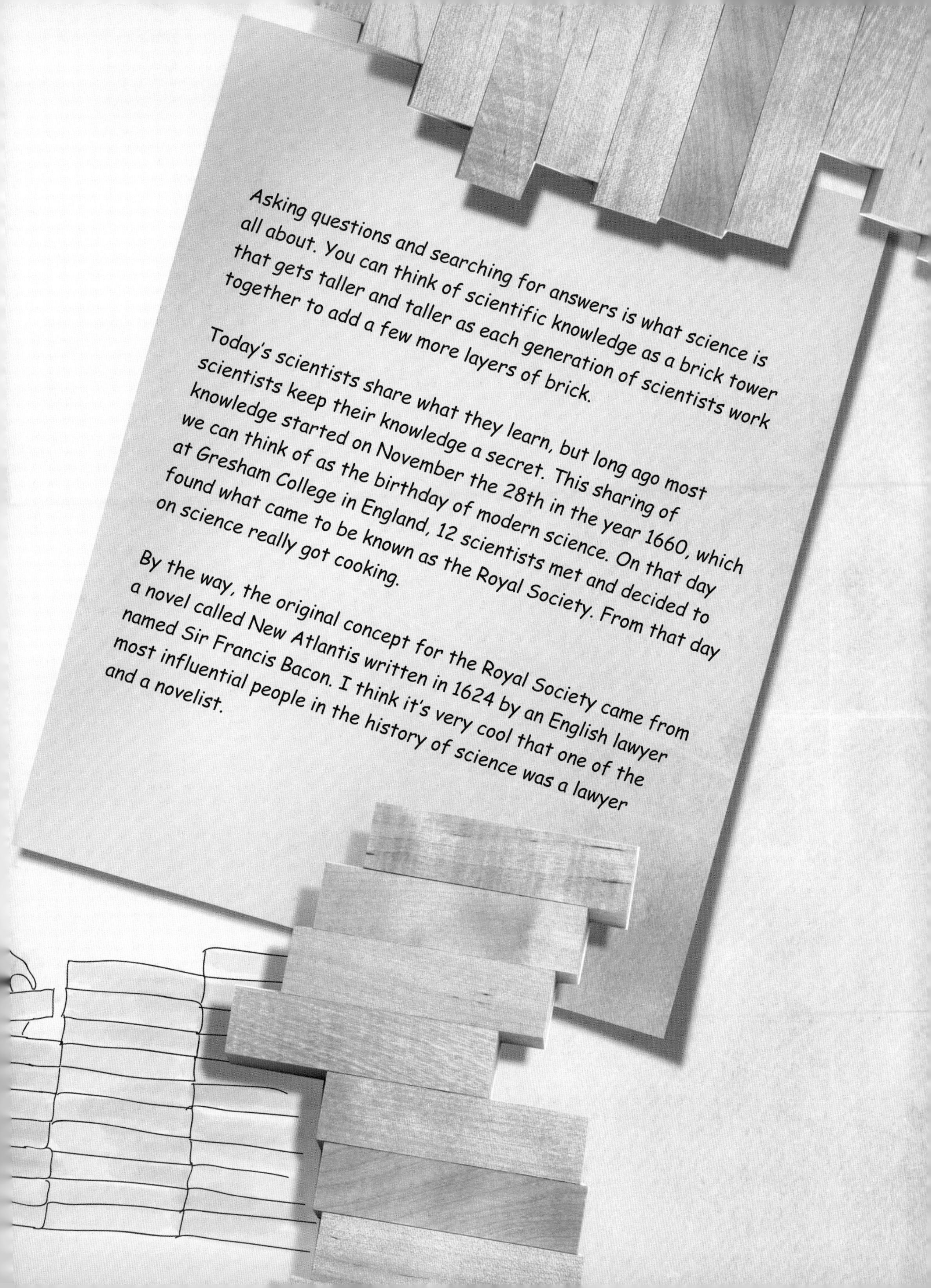

Asking questions and searching for answers is what science is all about. You can think of scientific knowledge as a brick tower that gets taller and taller as each generation of scientists work together to add a few more layers of brick.

Today's scientists share what they learn, but long ago most scientists keep their knowledge a secret. This sharing of knowledge started on November the 28th in the year 1660, which we can think of as the birthday of modern science. On that day at Gresham College in England, 12 scientists met and decided to found what came to be known as the Royal Society. From that day on science really got cooking.

By the way, the original concept for the Royal Society came from a novel called New Atlantis written in 1624 by an English lawyer named Sir Francis Bacon. I think it's very cool that one of the most influential people in the history of science was a lawyer and a novelist.

On the Field with the Pros
A Crocodile Tale

Today was one of the most important days of my life.
It started when my Aunt Janelle called me "trifling."
She said:
"Girl, you are full of questions.
You just might be the most trifling child I have ever known."
So I said:
"Aunt Janelle, I can ask all the questions I want."
And she said:
"Well Tamara, then you keep on asking those questions,
just don't expect to get any answers from me,
'cause you done passed me up a long time ago.
You go find out for yourself."

So I opened my laptop,
double-clicked Google™,
typed—"crocodile teeth bird clean," and pressed enter.
I had asked her about a story I heard when I was little,
how there's this bird that lives around crocodiles,
and they have this symbiotic thing going
where the crocodile opens his mouth real wide
and the bird hops in and cleans the crocodile's teeth,
pecking out little bits of food caught between the teeth,
and how the crocks are thankful and never eat the birds,
and it's a very cool story,
but lately I started asking myself, is it true?
I mean it still would be a cool story even if it's wasn't true,
but I needed to know, which is why I asked Aunt Janelle,
and why I ended up reading about it on the internet,
and why I'm pretty sure the whole thing is not true.
First of all, crocodiles don't need teeth cleaning.
They're constantly shedding their teeth
and replacing them with new ones,
so their teeth don't decay,
and besides, crocodile teeth are far apart;
no way food gets stuck.

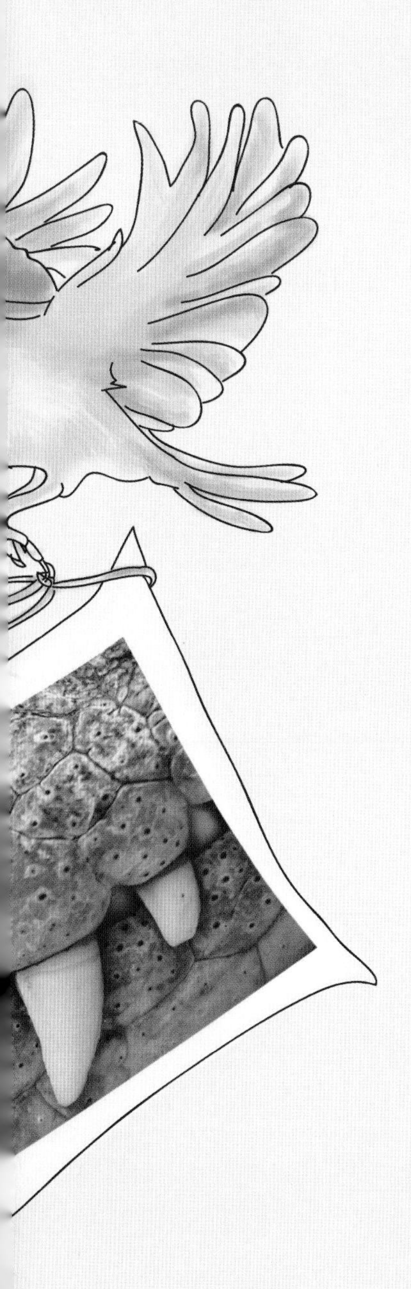

And nobody has ever gotten a picture of it,
let alone a video.
and with over a billion smart phones in the world
you'd think somebody would have gotten a picture.
Well actually there's one picture,
it's the only one,
you see it everywhere on the internet,
and it's a fake.

So the story is probably not true.
Birds and crocodiles are not mutuals.
So why is that such a big deal for me?

Well, this bird-crocodile thing is not just a story,
it's a story that's been around a long time:
It starts with this guy Herodotus who lived 2500 years ago,
and they even call him the Father of History,
and he describes it in detail.
Then Aristotle, who is like the most famous philosopher of all time,
he, too, writes about it in detail.
And sometimes they teach it in schools,
they even have children's books about it.
And then one day along comes me,
my Aunt Janelle calls me trifling and won't answer a question,
so I start reading a bunch of stuff from a bunch of different sources,
and come to the conclusion that it's probably not true.

I...ME...
looking things up and thinking it through,
with this brain in my head,
and it's like I'm on the field with the pros,
AND I HAVE THE POWER.
Sorry, I do get a little carried away.
But it's pretty cool,
questioning and searching,
and now that I know how good it feels,
I want more…to learn more,
and it's not just about good grades and getting a good job.
It's about wanting to be in the game,
to be on the field with the greats like Herodotus and Aristotle
and all the other great teachers,
to be one of the people who adds a little more to what we know.
And it all happened because my Aunt Janelle called me trifling
and stopped answering my questions,
and I can't help but wonder if she knew this would happen.
Hmmm...
She is definitely the smartest person in the family.

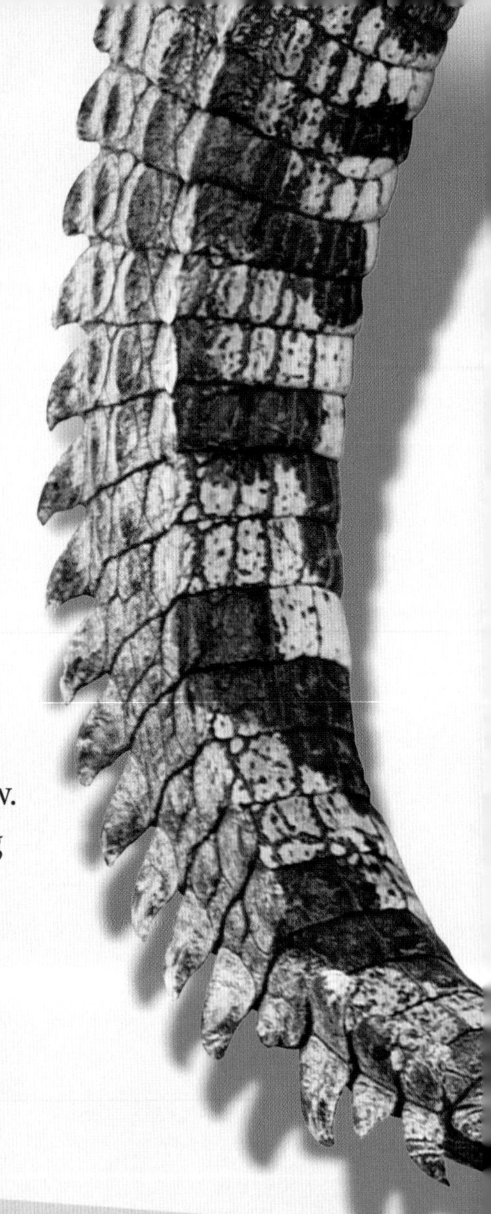

The history of knowledge has seen many battles between "authority" and "reason," and a whole lot of them involved Aristotle. Here's one of my favorites. Today everybody knows that there are craters on the moon, but back in the early 1600s nobody knew it until Galileo pointed a telescope at the moon and saw them. Up until then everybody thought the moon was perfectly smooth. That's what they thought because Aristotle had said so some 2,000 years earlier. So Galileo had made a big discovery, and if you wanted to know if he was right, all you had to do was look through a telescope. But most of Galileo's colleagues argued that there could be no craters on the moon because Aristotle had said is was perfectly smooth, and Aristotle was the authority. When Galileo asked them to look through the telescope and see with their own eyes, they refused.

Please understand I'm not criticizing Aristotle. Back then science wasn't even called science and he was at the very beginning of it, so it's unfair to blame him for making mistakes. The people who are to blame are those who refused to open their eyes. As the poem says: "RESEARCH and REASON is what I do, so sorry bird, you're just not true."

Sorry Bird

Crocodile bird, you are not real,
and that's not just the way I FEEL.
I've done the work, I've thought it through,
I KNOW there's no such bird as you.

Herodotus? You're the Father of History.
How you messed this up is a total mystery.
And Aristotle? Your rep is strong,
but this time, dude, you're totally wrong.

Some internet folks still say it's so,
but I don't care, I still say NO!
because I, as a rational human being,
will not agree just to be agreeing.

RESEARCH and REASON is what I do,
so sorry bird, you're just not true.

Detention, an A+ in Science And my Reggae Teacher

Our teachers have been teaching us the scientific method since first grade,
but this year Mr. Valente made us memorize this six step thing,
and then he told us we had to design our own experiments.
Sooooo…being the conscientious student that I am,
I decided to do it…my way.

Step # 1: Observation

I started by checking around for an observation,
and there it was: Mr. Valente himself,
how when he gets annoyed with me
(which happens almost every day)
he clenches his teeth and kind-of holds his breath,
and his face gets red like he's about to explode.

Step # 2: Question

Then I wondered:
what would it take to make Mr. Valente blow his top?

Now a scientist has to be very exact,
so I took my time,
thought it through,
and came up with an excellent hypothesis.

Step # 3: Hypothesis

If I expose Mr. Valente to an annoying stimulus
in the form of an invasive sound,
from an unknown source,
some time before the end of science class
Mr. Valente is bound to blow his stack.

Step # 4: Experiment

I found a recording of this very cool reggae beat.
hid a small Bluetooth speaker in the back of our science room,
and the plan was to hit play when Mr. Valente faced the other direction,
and then pause when he turned around.
I figured it would take four, maybe five cycles,
before Mr. Valente achieved critical mass,
and KA-BOOM! Experiment complete.

Step # 5: Data & Analysis

Cycle 1: The music begins,
Mr. Valente turns, clenches his teeth,
and, as the music stops, stares suspiciously around the room.
Cycle 2: The music begins,
Mr. Valente turns again, more quickly this time,
takes two rapid steps in the direction of the sound,
then, as the music stops again,
raises one eyebrow and shakes his head suspiciously.
Cycle 3: The music begins a third time,
Mr. Valente freezes but does not turn toward the music as before.
Then, ever so slowly at first,
and to the amazement of the entire class,
Mr. Valente broke into a dance that Bob Marley himself
would have been proud of,
and, to the cheers and applause of the entire class,
continued dancing for two minutes and twenty-six seconds.

Step # 6: Conclusion

Mr. Valente is a lot cooler than I thought,
and that science-man can dance.

When Mr. Valente returned my report
he was smiling cheek to cheek.
"A+ on the report," he said.
"and detention for a week."

Not all experiments are done in chemistry or physics labs. The experiment in this poem could be a real experiment in the psychology of human behavior, which is why Mr. Valente gave his student an A+.

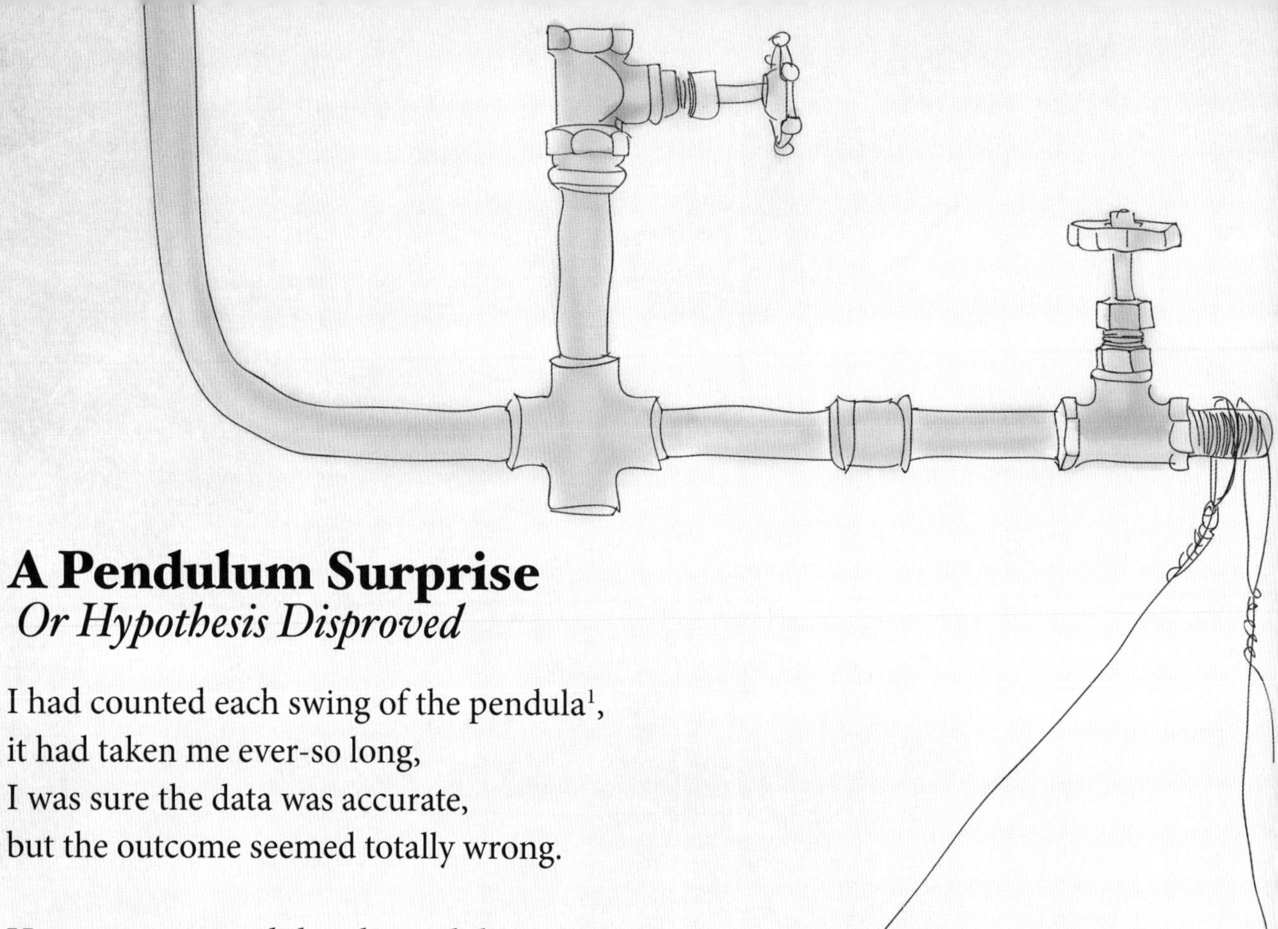

A Pendulum Surprise
Or Hypothesis Disproved

I had counted each swing of the pendula[1],
it had taken me ever-so long,
I was sure the data was accurate,
but the outcome seemed totally wrong.

How many times did each pendulum swing?
It's a little hard to explain,
but for both the baseball and bowling ball
the count was EXACTLY THE SAME.

No matter the size of the object,
and despite the difference in weight,
the number of swings is exactly the same
in the same gravitational state.

It's not what I had predicted,
it's quite an astonishing thing,
but I learned the controlling factor is simply
the length of the pendulum string.

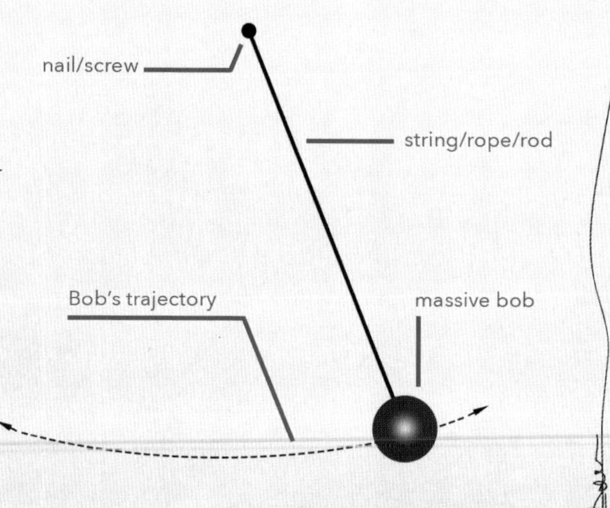

That's when I figured another thing out,
and it didn't take very long—
My experiment? Yes! A total success!
Even though my prediction wrong.

[1] *I used the Latin way to pluralize the word pendulum because I think it makes you guys sound really smart. Here are examples of scientific words that use the Latin way of pluralizing: one datum, lots of data; one bacterium, a zillion bacteria.*

Sometimes great scientific discoveries happen when experiments produce totally unexpected results. One famous example of this is the Rutherford gold foil experiment in 1908. (It's also known as the Geiger-Marsden Experiments, named after the two researchers who performed the experiments under the supervision of Rutherford.) Researchers shot alpha particles at a piece of gold foil having predicted that the particles would pass right through. Much to their surprise a few of the particles bounced back. As a result, the accepted Plum Pudding Model of atomic structure (electrons floating around likes plums in a pudding) was tossed out, and the new Rutherford Model (electrons orbiting around a tightly packed nucleus) was adopted. Since then the model of atomic structure has changed again. (The search to understand the structure of the atom is still going on, and I'll be telling you more later in this book.)

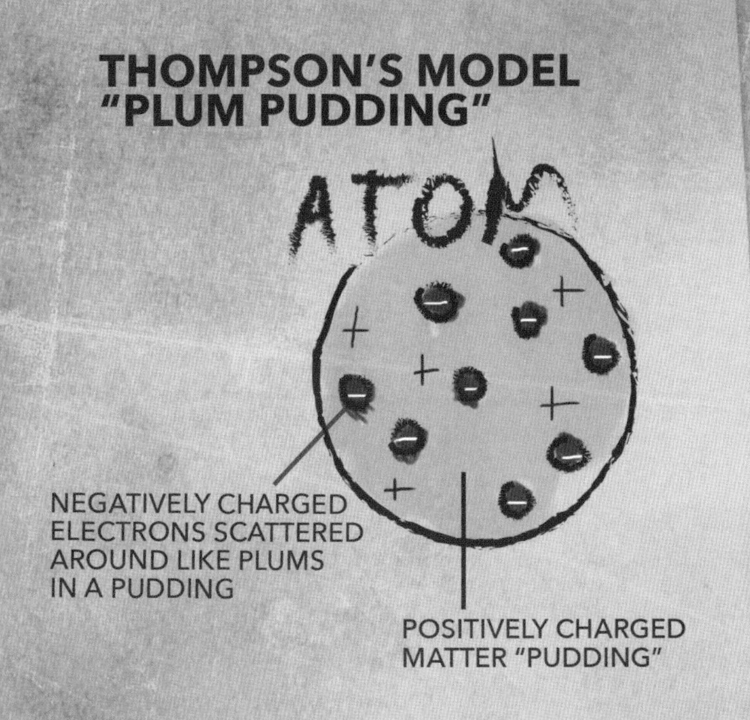

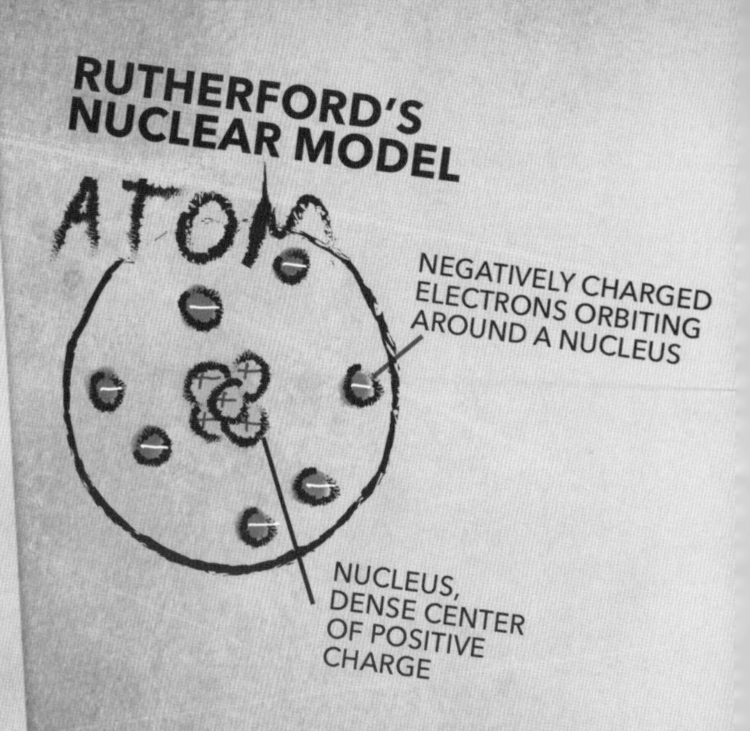

New Brain Magic
A Play In One Act

Cast of Characters —
Caroline: Bossy girl.
Javier: Funny boy.
Chorus: Three witches or wizards.

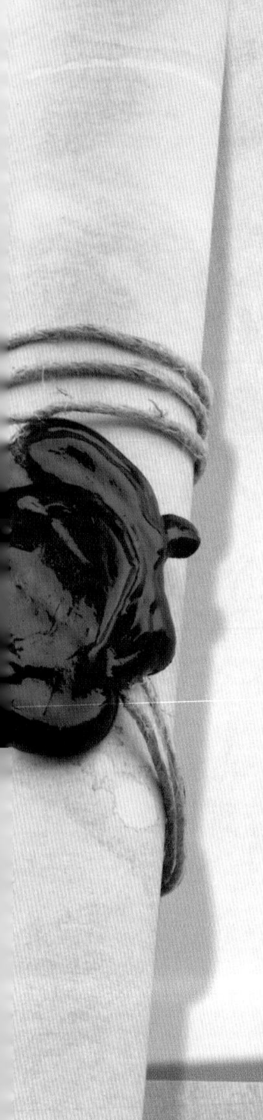

Chorus:
Thunder, lightening, wind, and rain.
All the things we must explain.
Ignorance is such a pain.
We need a scientific brain.

Caroline:
(Hesitates a moment as though thinking to herself, shakes her head affirmatively, raises a fist, and shouts.)
YES!
I'LL DO IT!

Javier:
What are you going to do, Caroline?

Alhazen
(Ibn al-Haytham)
965–1040

An Arab scientist and a pioneer of scientific method. "Truth is sought for its own sake."

Caroline:
With the help of these three witches… (She turns to the Chorus and waves her hand, as if presenting them to them to Javier.)
I am going to make a magic potion
that will turn normal brains
into brilliant scientific wonders.

Javier:
(With a mischievous grin, Javier turns to the audience and points his index finger to the side of his head with a twirling she-must-be-crazy gesture.)

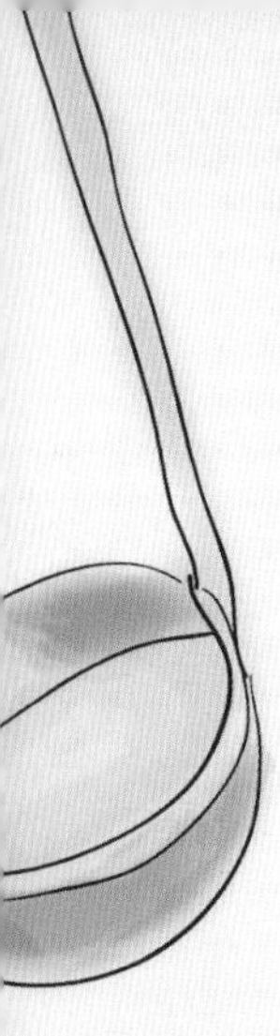

Caroline:
(Stomping her foot.)
Javier, get yourself over here.
I am going to do this
and I need your help.

Javier:
(Saluting like a soldier.)
Yesssss, ma'am!
I'm happy to help!
(Aside in a stage whisper.)
It's never a good idea
to say "no" to Caroline.

Caroline:
Stop that fooling around, Javier.
Grab that pot,
put it over here,
and let's get to work.
(Javier obediently places a large pot on a stool center stage.)

Caroline:
Let's see...
what comes first?
Any ideas, funny boy?

Javier:
Well, a scientific brain finds answers,
but you can't find answers
if you don't ask questions.
So we need to make a brain that questions everything.

Caroline:
Hmm!
Alright, witches,
we need a little help here.
We need a questioning spell.

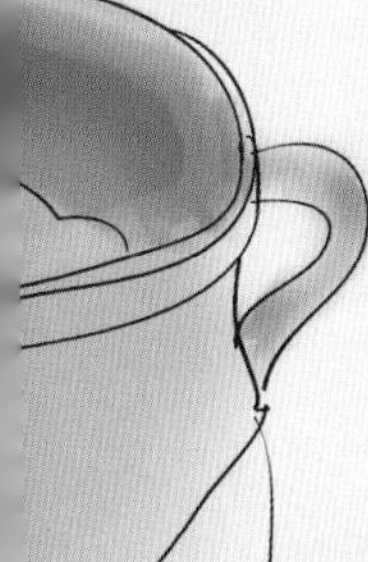

Aristotle
384-322 BCE

Ancient Greek scientists didn't do experiments. They understood things like temperature and speed but without thermometers and clocks they had no way to measure them. Does that mean that it's important for scientists to be able to measure things?
YES! YES! YES! YES!

Roger Bacon
1214-1294

English scientist who used repeated cycles of observation, hypothesis, and experimentation. He also stressed the importance of independent verification.

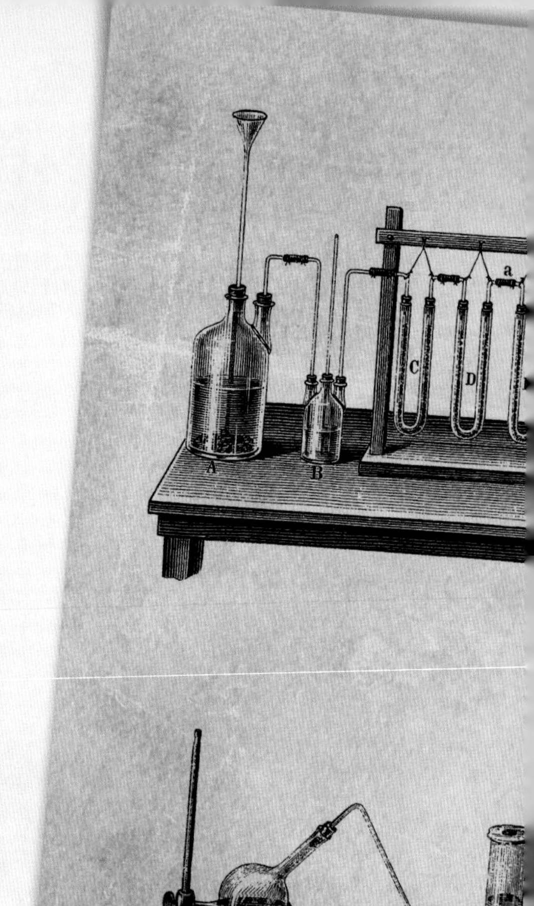

Chorus:
(Chorus gathers round the pot and together recites the following chant three times. As they chant they circle the pot in a rhythmic dance using one hand to shoot magic rays at the container. Each has the words printed on a piece of paper. At the end, they tear their papers into little pieces and drop them into the pot.)

Teacher! Preacher! Poet! King!
We can question everything!
What and when and where and who
and how can we be sure it's true?

(Repeat 3 times, progressively more dramatic.)

Caroline:
Ok, that's enough.

(Turning to Javier.)
Not bad, Jav.
So what comes next?

Javier:
Well, believe it or not,
a scientist has got to be a good guesser.
They start with a question,
something like, "Do plants need sunshine to grow?"
Then they think of everything they know about plants,
and everything they know about sunshine,
and all the possibilities they can imagine,
and make their best guess at an answer.
Scientists call it a "hypothesis,"
which means a "really smart guess."

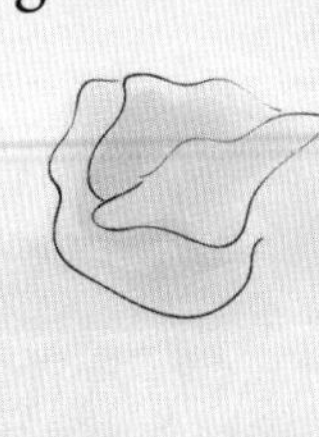

Caroline:
Alright, witches.
let's have a hypothesis spell.

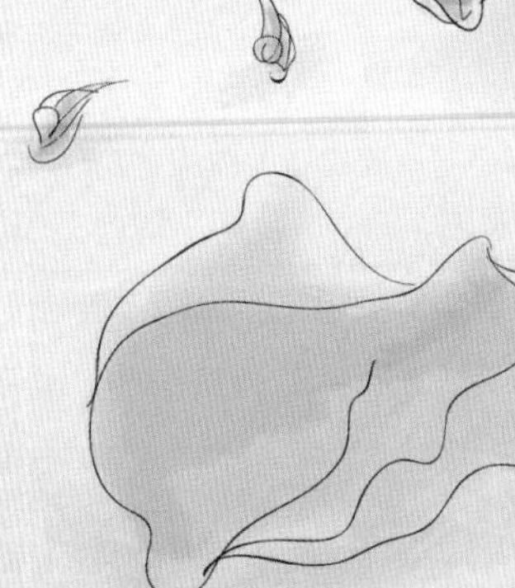

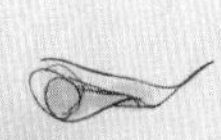

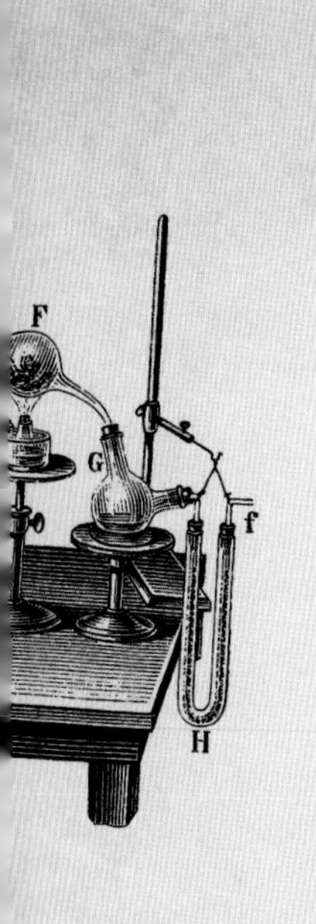

Chorus:
(Same dance; paper into the pot.)
We do not know! We must confess!
So now it's time to make a guess.
Think long and wide and high and deep,
then close your eyes and take a leap!
(Repeat 3 times, progressively more dramatic.)

— PLEASE HELP ME! —

To make the rhyme work, please pronounce "data" like "beta," and for "investigator" drop the "r" and say "investigata."

Caroline:
Ok, Javier, you're on a roll.
What next?

Javier:
Well, now the scientists have to figure out
if they guessed right.
They call it "testing the hypothesis."
(Turning to the Chorus.)
And what do we use to test a hypothesis?

Chorus:
(Same dance; pieces of paper into the pot.)
Experiment! Collect the data!
Factual investigator!
Don't be nervous. Just relax.
Take your time and get the facts.
(Repeat 3 times, progressively more dramatic.)

Caroline:
(Big smile. She obviously knows the answer.)
And when you finish your experiment,
what do you do with all that data?

Chorus:
(Same dance; pieces of paper into the pot.)
Here's the data! Black and white!
Are we wrong or are we right?
Analysis is what we do
to tell us if our guess is true!
(Repeat 3 times, progressively more dramatic.)

Francis Bacon 1561-1626

An English scientist who was totally committed to the process of experimentation. Author of "Novum Organum," which means "New Organ," which is why I named this play "New Brain Magic." By the way, he was no relation to Roger Bacon.

Caroline:

Alright.
The moment of truth.
Witches and wizards, do your duty!

(Witches move through the audience [or class] sprinkling bits of torn paper from the pot over the heads of the students. Each makes a gesture or strikes a pose to indicate that he/she has been turned into a scientific genius as they shout out genius-kid scientific stuff. Then, when finished…)

Caroline:

Alright.
Let's see if this worked.

(Cast forms line facing audience, as cast and audience, led by Caroline, recite all the chants together.)

Thunder, lightning, wind, and rain.
All the things we must explain.
Ignorance is such a pain.
We need a scientific brain.

Teacher! Preacher! Poet! King!
We can question everything!
What and when and where and who
and how can we be sure it's true?

We do not know! We must confess!
So now it's time to make a guess.
Think long and wide and high and deep,
then close your eyes and take a leap!

Experiment! Collect the data!
Factual investigator!
Don't be nervous. Just relax.
Take your time and get the facts.

Here's the data! Black and white!
Are we wrong or are we right?
Analysis is what we do
to tell us if our guess is true!

Thunder! …Lightning! …Wind and rain!
Natural things! …We must explain!
Ignorance is such a pain!
WE NEED…A SCIENTIFIC…BRAIN!

I bet you guys can search the internet and come up with about thousand "genius-kid scientific stuff" to shout out at the end of this play. Here are a few examples to get you started.

- E = mc2 (Energy is equal to mass times the speed of light squared.)

- The acceleration of gravity on planet Earth is 9.8 meters per second squared.

- The DNA molecule is the shape of a double spiral helix.

- The speed of light in a vacuum is 299,792 kilometers per second.

- In outer space objects become weightless but retain the same mass.

- Eukaryote cells of the animal world possess an inner cell nuclear membrane but no outer cell wall.

- Prokaryote cells of the bacterial world possess an outer cell wall but no inner cell nuclear membrane.

-Your turn...

Progress

Great-grandpa had a gramophone that weighed a hundred pounds.
Grandpa had a hi-fi that stood four feet off the ground.
Papa had components stacked in stages like a rocket.
And for me it was a Walkman[2] I could fit inside my pocket.
But my daughter got an iPod[3] that was even smaller yet,
and my grandson's iPod Nano[4] seems as small as it can get.

We threw away those old machines cause they were obsolete,
but the music they once played for us will stay forever sweet,
for the beauty of the sound can survive a thousand years,
and progress? Well it's just the way we get it in our ears.

[2] "Walkman" is a registered trademark of Sony Corporation.
[3] "iPod" is a registered trademark of the Apple Corporation.
[4] "iPod Nano" is a registered trademark of the Apple Corporation.

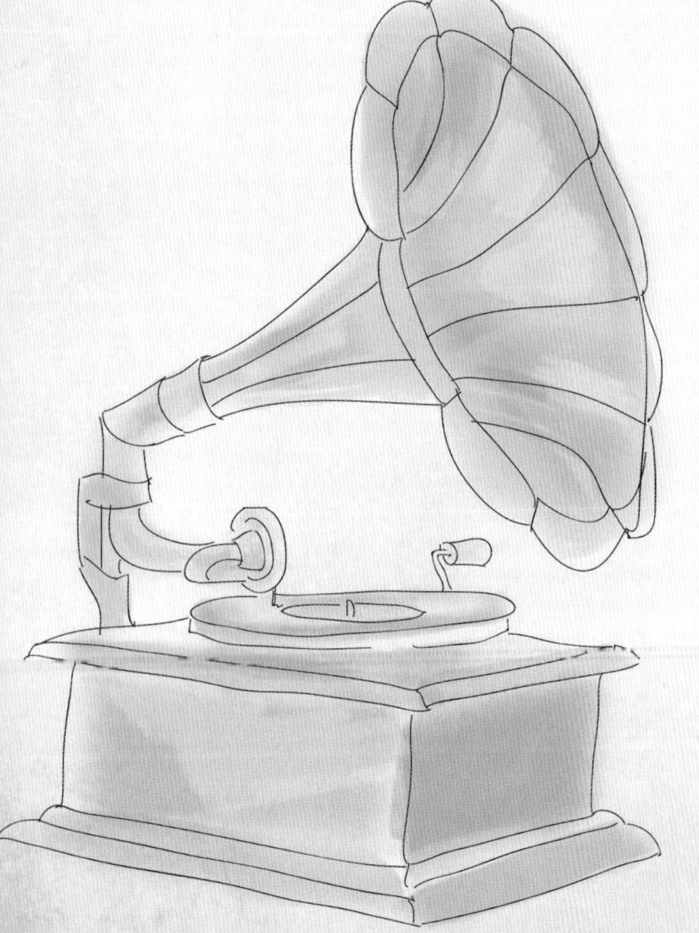

Gramophone? Hi-fi? Component stereo? Walkman? Each of these represented a spectacular advance in the way people listened to music. Today, most people have no idea what they are. That's because science has begun to change our lives at lightning speed. The first smart phone was introduced in the year 2000, and less than 20 years later people can't imagine life without our little handheld computers. So...what's next?

Mad Scientist

It's totally unfair.
It's totally not right.
I study all day long at school,
I study every night.

How did this ever happen?
Is there someone who's to blame?
Oh yes, there is a bad-guy, and
I even know his name.

Edison invented the light bulb,
turning nighttime into day,
but he didn't stop to think about
the price I'd have to pay.

Shouldn't scientists consider
the pain that they might cause
by the real-world application
of their scientific laws?

If it weren't for the light bulb,
oh how lovely night would be.
I'd sit quietly in the dark
watching movies on TV.

But no, that nasty light-bulb
makes me study day and night.
IT'S TOTALLY UNFAIR!
IT'S TOTALLY NOT RIGHT!

This poem is a playful treatment of a serious question. Should scientists invent things without considering the possible harm they might cause?

In the 200 years between Mary Shelley's novel, Frankenstein, and Michael Crichton's movie, Jurassic Park, there have been a zillion books and movies about those brilliant mad-scientists who start out with good intentions but, in the end, are destroyed by their own creation.
So here are some questions to think about. Would the world be better off if we had never invented the atom bomb? Should scientists clone human beings? If we make a medicine that could keep people alive for a thousand years, should we use it? Should ethics impose limits on science?

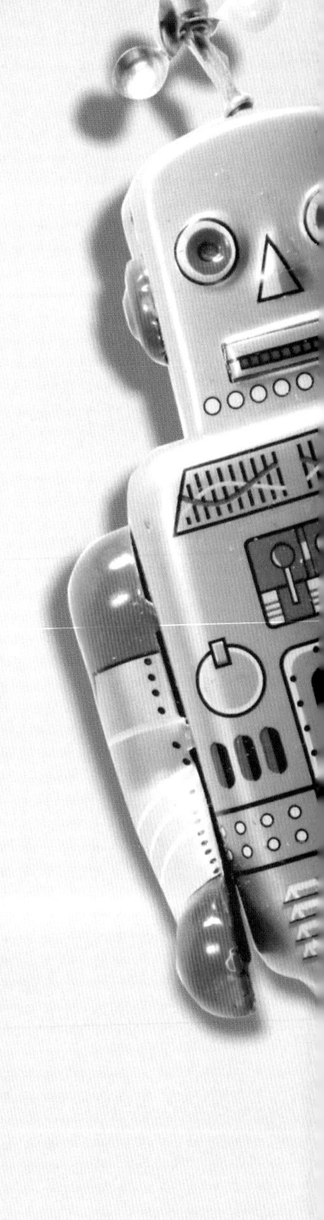

Knowledge in Motion

Isaac Newton declared the magnificent notion
that three basic laws governed objects in motion.
This giant idea was the ultimate thing,
and for almost three centuries Newton was king.

But then Einstein declared, it's important to know,
that these laws only work if the motion is slow,
but as speeds start approaching the swiftness of light,
the three laws of Sir Isaac are no longer right.

So you see how our knowledge keeps inching along.
It seems perfect today, but tomorrow it's wrong.
And who will be next to propose something new?
First Newton, then Einstein, and next...Maybe you?

Isaac Newton (1642–1726/1727),
English scientist

Albert Einstein
(14 March 1879–18 April 1955) ,
German-born theoretical physicist

MAYBE YOU
(2018-future)

An Invitation

Some years ago it became my life's dream to write a bunch of poems about science; poems that would be both fun and instructional; poems to simultaneously entertain you and help you become life-long learners.

I've been at it now for over 20 years, and I have begun to understand that this little book and the ones to follow, are just a first step, and that the next step depends on you.

That's why I am inviting you to join me in the wonderful work of awakening the joy of powerful thinking in the minds of your generation. We humans are proud of our tall buildings and our 2000 year old aqueducts and our 4000 year old pyramids, and we should be. But what we can be most proud of is that pocketful of simple yet powerful ideas that made every one of those things possible. I invite you to join me in helping to keep those ideas healthy and strong among your generation.

Look back through the pages of this book, pick out a piece that you really like, and then do something with it and send it to me. You might make a video of you and your friends performing it; or create your own original illustration or animation; or write your own original poem or play; or simply write your thoughts after reading it; or maybe something else I can't even imagine. As time goes by we at Brod Bagert's Heart of Science will be selecting some of your material and (with your permission) sharing it with others just like you.

I believe that many of you will accept this invitation and have fun doing it. There may even be a few of you who will like it a lot, a few of you for whom it will become the joy of your lives, as it has been in mine. Maybe you'll be the ones to help take Brod Bagert's Heart of Science to a whole new level. And maybe, eventually, you'll become the stars that bring light to the night skies of your generation. Please accept this as your invitation.

Dedication

To my wonderful grandson, Quinten.
B.B.

To my dear mother, Tatiana.
N.K.

Publishing Information

Published by Living Road Press
San Antonio, TX

ISBN 978-1732151512

Acknowledgements

Thanks to Cathy Barker, the classroom teacher who insisted I write poems about science; to Carol Espensen, my editor/publisher whose passion for this project may exceed my own; to Natalia King, whose artistic vision is a treasure; to Debby, my wife who makes all things possible; and to my wonderful 5,000 plus "Muse Project Teachers," whose ongoing interest in science-content literature inspired me to keep writing for the 15 years lead-time it took to make this dream a reality.